SRA

OPEN COURT
READING

# Finding
# Friends

SRA

A Division of The McGraw·Hill Companies

Columbus, Ohio

# — PROGRAM AUTHORS —

Marilyn Jager Adams       Anne McKeough       Gerald H. Treadway, Jr.

Carl Bereiter       Marsha Roit       Michael Pressley

Marlene Scardamalia       Jan Hirshberg       Marcy Stein

Grateful acknowledgment is given to the following publishers and copyright owners for permissions granted to reprint selections from their publications. All possible care has been taken to trace ownership and secure permission for each selection included. In case of any errors or omissions, the Publisher will be pleased to make suitable acknowledgments in future editions.

## Acknowledgments

GINGER. Copyright © 1997 by Charlotte Voake. Reprinted by permission of Candlewick Press Inc., Cambridge, MA, on behalf of Walker Books Ltd., London. From THE LONELY PRINCE by Max Bolliger. Copyright © 1981 by Max Bolliger. Reproduced by arrangement with Simon & Schuster Books for Young Readers, Simon & Schuster Children's Publishing Division. All rights reserved. "Making Friends" from NATHANIEL TALKING. Copyright © 1988 by Eloise Greenfield. Reprinted by permission of Nancy Gallt Literary Agency. Illustration © Jan Spivey Gilchrist from Nathaniel Talking by Eloise Greenfield. Reprinted by permission of Pippin Properties, Inc.

## Photo Credits

**56 (bl)** © Courtesy of the Kimbell Art Museum, Fort Worth, Texas; **56 (r)** © Scala/Art Resource, NY.; **56 (tl)** © Art Resource, NY.

www.sra4kids.com

## SRA/McGraw-Hill
*A Division of The McGraw-Hill Companies*

Send all inquiries to:
SRA/McGraw-Hill
8787 Orion Place
Columbus, OH 43240-4027

Printed in Mexico by RR Donnelley & Sons Company's wholly-owned subsidiary, Impresora Donneco Internacional

ISBN 0-07-602715-5

2 3 4 5 6 7 8 9 RRM 10 09 08 07 06 05

# Table of Contents
## Finding Friends

# GINGER

by Charlotte Voake

Ginger was a lucky cat.

He lived with
a little girl
who made him
delicious meals

and gave him
   a beautiful basket,

where he would curl up . . .
and close his eyes.

Here he is, fast asleep.

But here he is again,
  WIDE AWAKE.

What's this?

A kitten!

"He'll be a nice new
friend for you, Ginger,"
said the little girl.

But Ginger
didn't want a new friend,
especially one like this.
Ginger hoped the
kitten would
go away,

but he didn't.

Everywhere
Ginger went,
the kitten followed,
springing out
from behind
doors,

leaping onto Ginger's back,
even eating Ginger's food!

What a naughty
kitten!

But what upset Ginger
more than anything
was that whenever
he got into his
beautiful basket,
the kitten always
climbed in too,

and
the little
girl didn't
do anything
about it.

So Ginger decided to leave home.

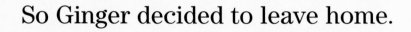

He went out
through the cat flap
and he didn't come back.

The kitten waited for a while,
then he got into
Ginger's basket.

It wasn't the same without Ginger.

The kitten
played
with some
flowers,

then he found
somewhere
to sharpen
his claws.

The little girl
found him on the table
drinking some milk.

"You naughty kitten!" she said.

"I thought you
were with Ginger.
Where is he anyway?"

She looked
in Ginger's
basket,

but of course he wasn't there.

16

"Perhaps he's eating his food," she said.
But Ginger wasn't there either.

"I hope
he's not upset,"
she said.
"I hope
he hasn't
run away."

She put on her galoshes and went out into the garden, and that is where she found him;

a very wet, sad, cold Ginger, hiding under a bush.

The little girl
carried Ginger
and the kitten
inside.
"It's a pity
you can't
be friends,"
she said.

She gave
  Ginger a special meal.

She gave the kitten
a little plate
of his own.

Then she tucked Ginger
into his own
warm basket.

All she could find for the kitten
to sleep in was a little tiny
cardboard box.

But the kitten
didn't mind, because
cats love cardboard boxes
(however small they are).

So when the little girl
went in to see
the two cats
again,

THIS is how she found them.

And now Ginger
and the naughty kitten
get along very well . . .

most of the time!

# The Lonely Prince

Max Bolliger

*illustrated by Bonnie MacKain*

There was once a little Prince called William. He lived with his parents, the King and the Queen, in a huge castle surrounded by a beautiful green park.

William was very spoiled. He was
given everything that he wanted. He
*should* have been happy, but he wasn't.
He didn't laugh and he didn't cry—he
always looked sad.

The King and the Queen were very
worried. "Why do you look so sad?"
they asked anxiously. "You have every
toy that money can buy. Whatever can
you want?"

William thought for a moment. "I haven't got a hot-air balloon," he said. "If that's what you want," sighed the King and the Queen, "you shall have one. Now do cheer up!"

All day long, William played with his
balloon. He filled it up with air and
drifted gently in it over the castle and
the wide green park. Then he floated
down again. But still William didn't laugh
and he didn't cry. He just looked sad.

The King and the Queen became even more worried. "You have every toy that money can buy *and* a hot-air balloon," they fussed. "Whatever can you want now?"

"I want a lion in a cage," said William.
"Oh dear, very well," sighed the King
and the Queen, "if that's what you want,
you shall have one. Now do cheer up!"

All day long, William played with his lion. He teased and tickled him with a stick and fed him pieces of meat. But still William didn't laugh and he didn't cry. He just looked sad.

The King and the Queen worried more
and more. "You have every toy that
money can buy *and* a hot-air balloon
*and* a lion in a cage," they fretted.
"Whatever can you still want?"

"I want to command an army," said William.

"Very well," sighed the King and the Queen, "if that's what you want, you shall command a battalion of soldiers. Now do cheer up!"

William had the soldiers marching,
fighting, and riding their horses all
day long.

But still William didn't laugh and
he didn't cry. He just looked sadder
than ever.

Then one day, when William was
walking in the park, he saw the
gardener's boy. He was sitting outside
the gardener's house, cuddling a rabbit.
He gave it dandelions to eat and
stroked its long fur.

William watched them. Then he
thought, "I have all the toys that money
can buy, and a hot-air balloon and a lion
in a cage and a battalion of soldiers but
what I would really like more than
anything else is a rabbit to stroke and
feed with dandelion leaves."

 37

William ran up to the boy. "Please give
me your rabbit," he said.

"No," said the boy, cuddling the rabbit
closer. "He's mine. I don't want to give
him to you."

So William ran back to his parents in the castle. "I've got all the toys that money can buy and a hot-air balloon and a lion in a cage and a battalion of soldiers, but what I would really like more than anything else is a rabbit."

"If a rabbit will make you happy," said the King and the Queen together, "you shall have a rabbit at once."

All the next day, William played with
his rabbit. He picked him up, stroked
his long ears and gave him green leaves
and carrots to eat. But still William
didn't laugh and he didn't cry. He
looked even sadder than before.

"I don't want just *any* rabbit," he said.
"I want the gardener's boy's rabbit."

43

William hurried back to the gardener's
boy. "Will you give me your rabbit?" he
said. "You can have all my toys."

"No," said the boy.

44

"Please give me your rabbit," repeated
William. "You can have all my toys and
a hot-air balloon."

"No," said the boy.

 45

"*Please* give me your rabbit," William begged for the third time. "You can have all my toys and a hot-air balloon and a lion in a cage *and* a battalion of soldiers."

"No," said the boy again.

And suddenly William felt so
miserable that he burst into tears.

The gardener's boy was very upset
and said to William kindly, "I can't give
you my rabbit because I love him and
he knows me, but we can play with him
together."

All the next day Prince William and
the gardener's boy played happily with
the rabbit. They stroked his long fur
and gave him dandelion leaves to eat.

 49

That night, when the King and the
Queen came to tuck William up in bed
they were amazed to see that he didn't
look sad at all. "Whatever is the
matter?" they said.

Then something very strange happened; William started to smile. "Now I know what I want more than anything else in the whole world," he said. "I want a friend!"

The King and the Queen were very
dismayed. "But we can't *give* you a
friend," they said. "You have to find
friends for yourself."

"But I *have* found one," said William.

And, for the very first time, he laughed.

# Making Friends

Eloise Greenfield

*illustrated by Jan Spivey Gilchrist*

when I was in kindergarten
this new girl came in our class one day
and the teacher told her to sit beside me
and I didn't know what to say
so I wiggled my nose and made my bunny face
and she laughed
then she puffed out her cheeks
and she made a funny face
and I laughed
so then
we were friends

54

*Children Playing at Dockside.* c.1939–1942. **William H. Johnson.** National Museum of American Art, Smithsonian Institution, Washington, DC.

*Happy Age, Golden Age.* c.1716–17. **Antoine Watteau.** Oil on wood. $8\frac{1}{4} \times 9\frac{5}{8}$ in. Courtesy of the Kimbell Art Museum, Fort Worth, Texas.

*The Rooster.* 1928. **Marc Chagall.** Thyssen-Bornemisza, Madrid, Spain. ©2001 Artists Rights Society (ARS), New York/ADAGP, Paris.

# Glossary

# B

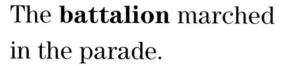

The **battalion** marched in the parade.

# C

Did the **cat** jump onto the couch?

Mother kissed the baby's **cheek.**

The bird had
sharp **claws.**

## D

The **dandelion** was
growing in the field.

## F

The **flap** on the door
was for the dog.

# G

Jenny's **galoshes** keep her feet dry.

The **gardener** took care of the garden.

# H

Dana rode the **horse** at the farm.

The **hot-air balloon** floated above the trees.

# K

The **kitten** played with the yarn.

# M

Jose drank **milk** with his lunch.

Granddad paid for our tickets with **money.**

# P

The **prince** is the son of the king and queen.

# Q

Did the **queen** wear her crown?

# R

The **rabbit** hopped in the grass.

# S

The **soldier** carried the flag.